The BEST TRADITIONAL *Piano Etudes*

Book 1

LYNN FREEMAN OLSON

The Best Traditional Piano Etudes are those that have not only met with universal teacher and student approval but also serve their purpose very well—they can be positive ingredients in building a ready technique. Today we have many eras of etudes to sift through—there is not time for them all! This series presents the editor's choices in modern editions that are easy to read. The etudes in each book are grouped according to general purpose.

EARLY INTERMEDIATE

Cover design: Linda Prendergast   Original cover art: Marla Tarbox

1.

1 - 8

ORIGINAL KEY

Hermann Berens

E MAJOR

1 - 15

F MINOR

RHYTHMIC VARIATION

arr. L.F.O

Béla Bartók

3.

Béla Bartók

Moderato

poco rit.

4. 2-5

Béla Bartók

Moderato

poco rit.

5.

2-5   2-12 - Ancentive

Emil Söchting

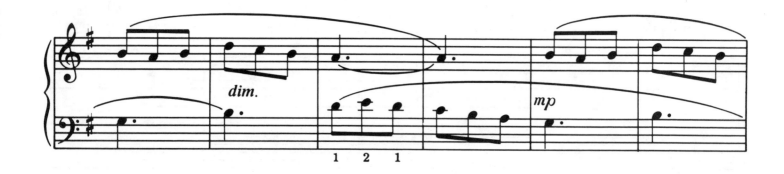

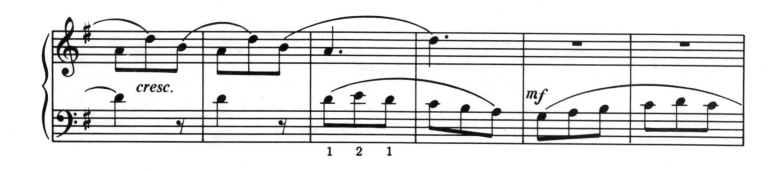

6.

2-26 2-19 Inc.

Cornelius Gurlitt

Con moto

7.

Louis Köhler

Allegretto

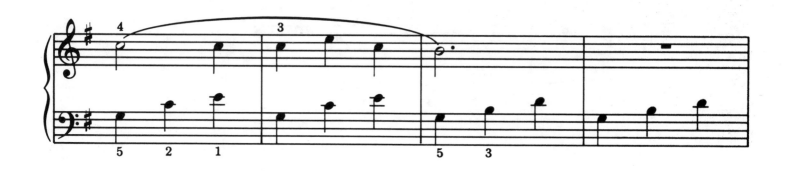

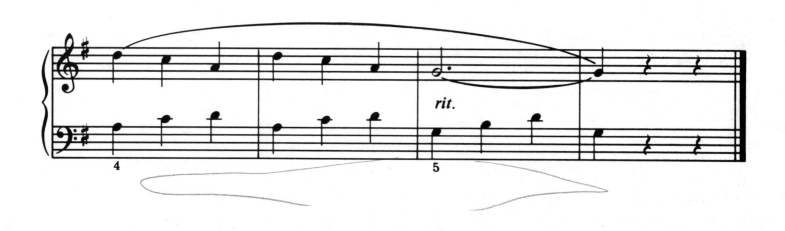

8.

faster
2-26

memorize
2019

Dmitri Kabalevsky

Moderato

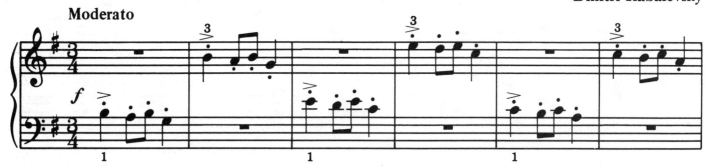

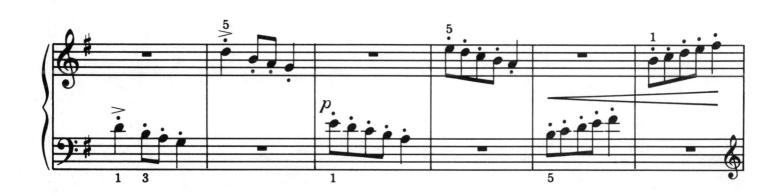

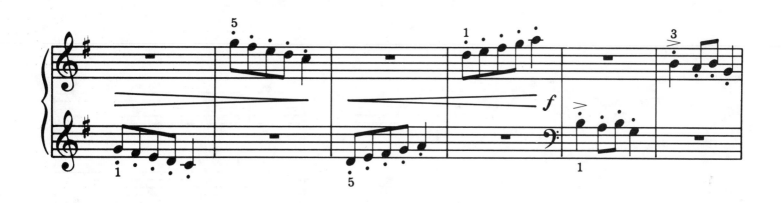

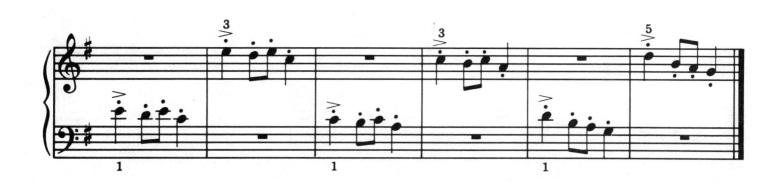

9.

Dmitri Kabalevsky

10.

3-26

Ludvig Schytte

Allegro moderato

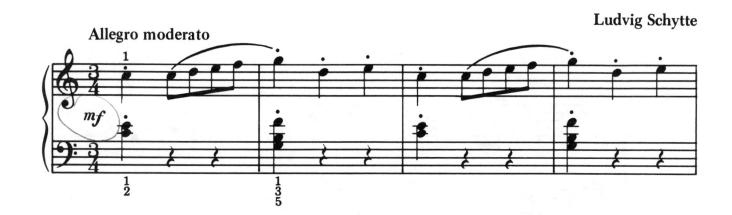

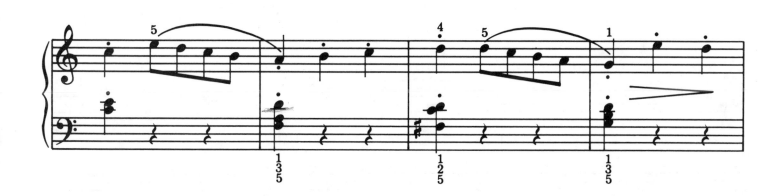

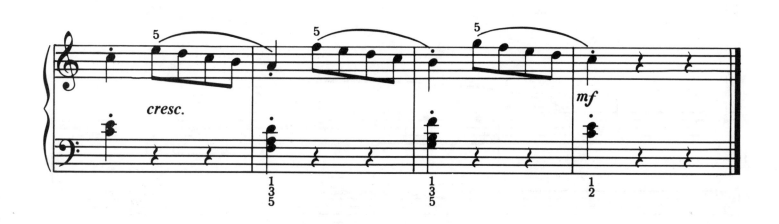

11.

Felix Le Couppey

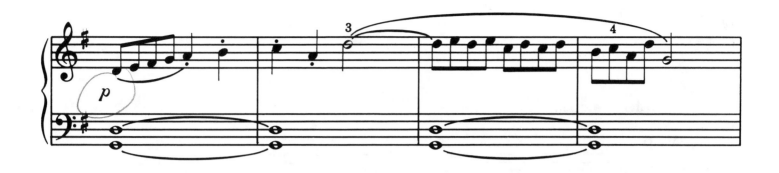

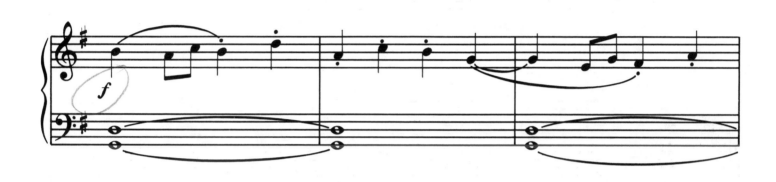

12.

Allegro moderato

Ludvig Schytte

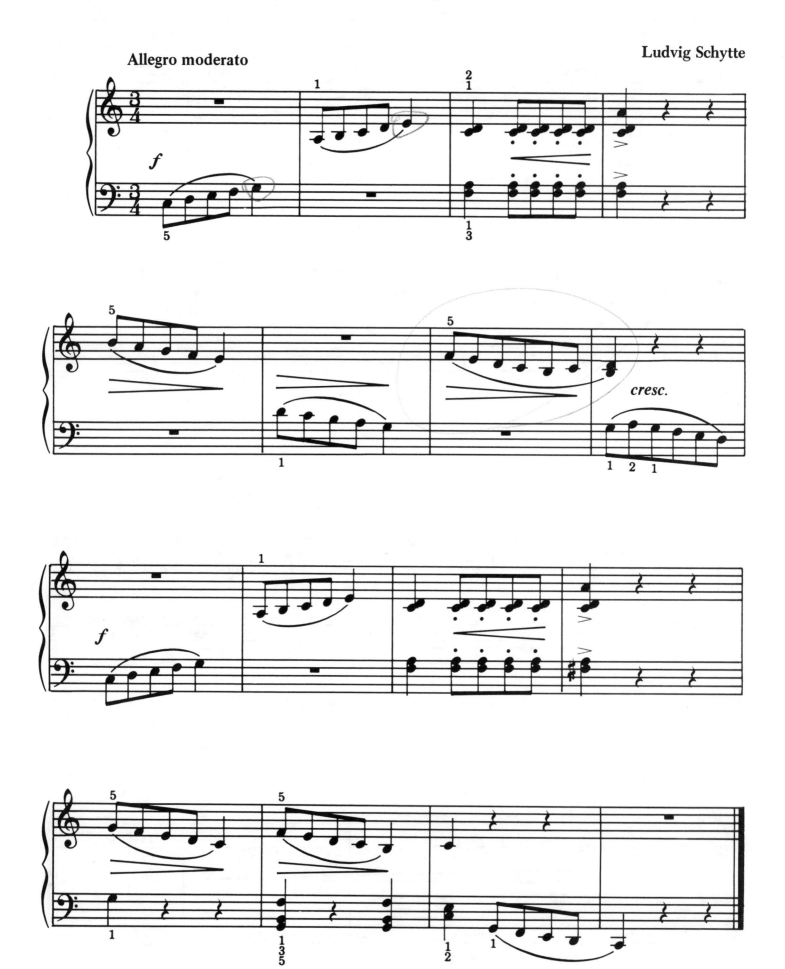

14.

Dmitri Kabalevsky

Vivo, giocoso

15.

Cornelius Gurlitt

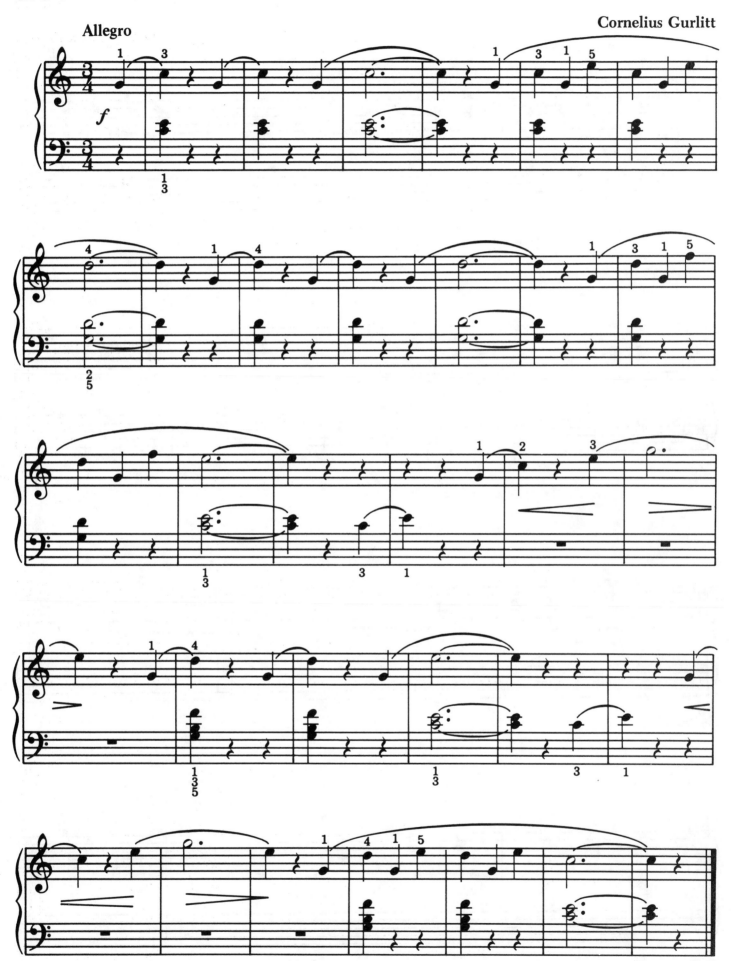

16.

6 - 4

Allegretto

Streabbog (Jean Louis Gobbearts)

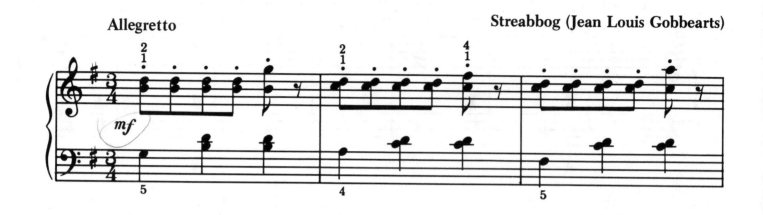

17.

G-11

Cornelius Gurlitt

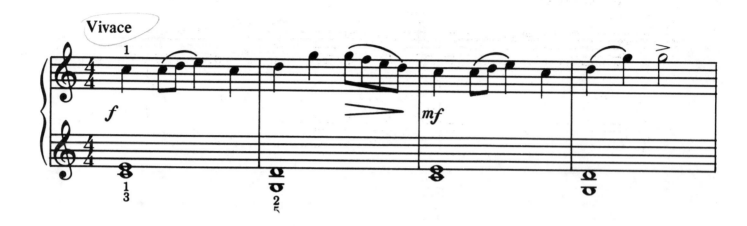

18. 6-16

Ludvig Schytte

Allegro moderato

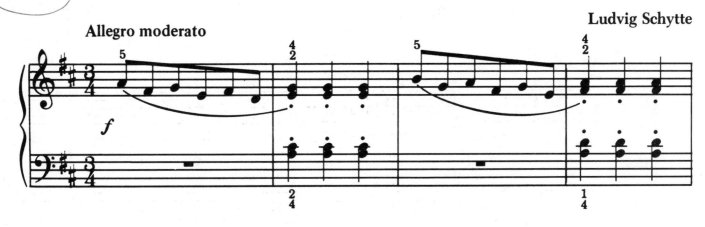

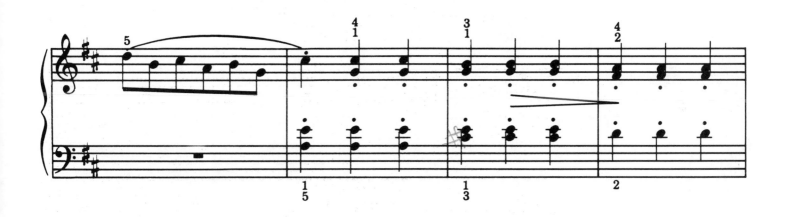

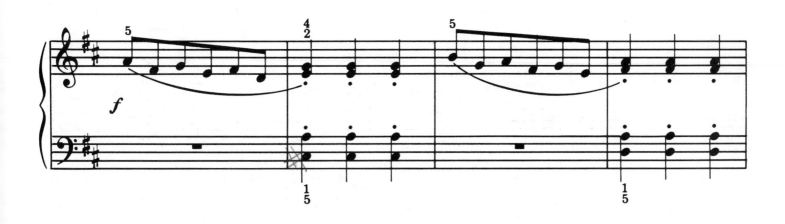

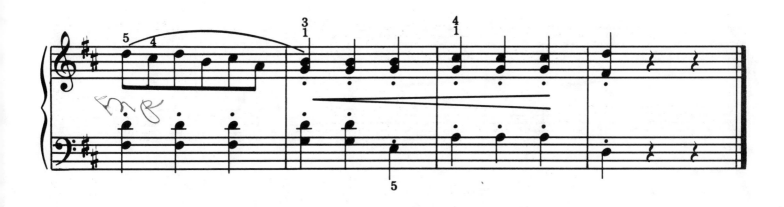

19.

6 - 24

Ludvig Schytte

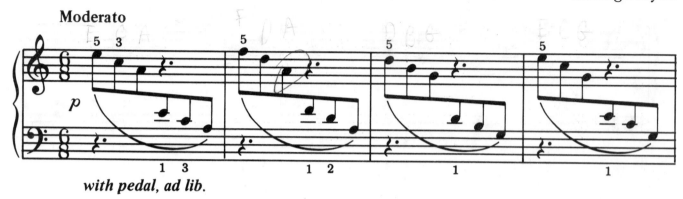

Moderato

p

with pedal, ad lib.

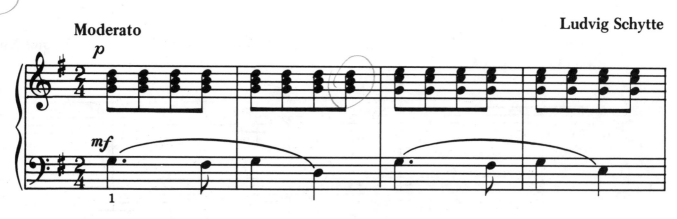

20.

7-1

Moderato

Ludvig Schytte

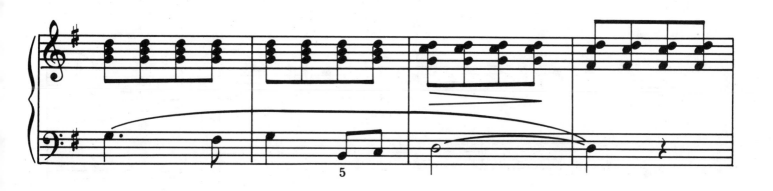

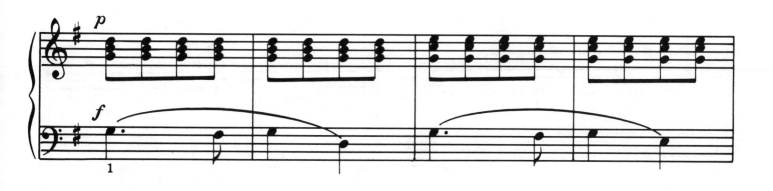

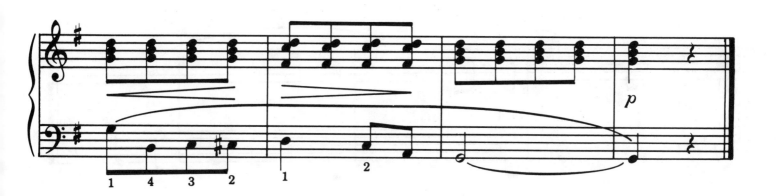

21.

7 - 8

Louis Köhler

Andante

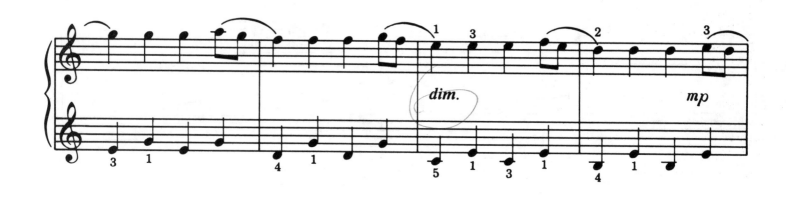

22.

Moderato

Ferdinand Beyer

23.

Felix Le Couppey

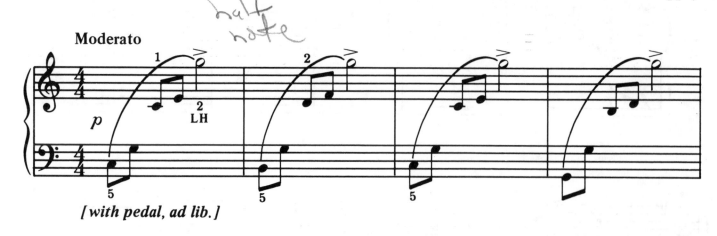

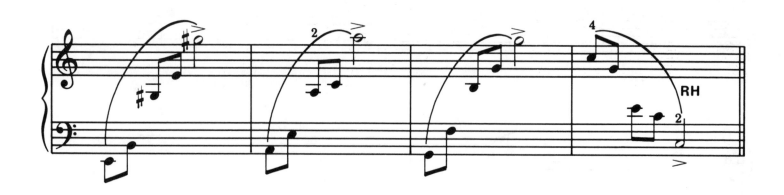

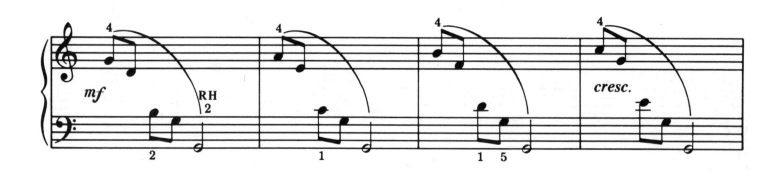

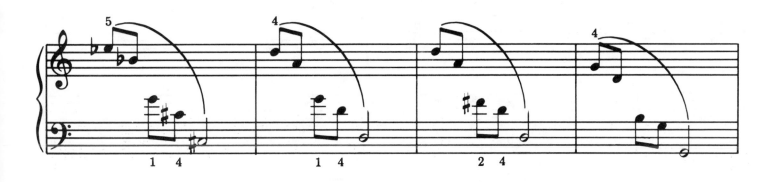

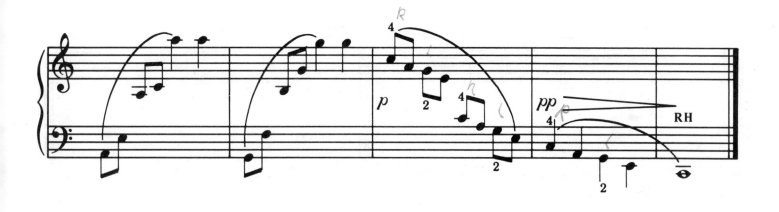

24.

8-12

9-14

isolate mesures

Andante

Louis Köhler

cantabile

25.

Cornelius Gurlitt

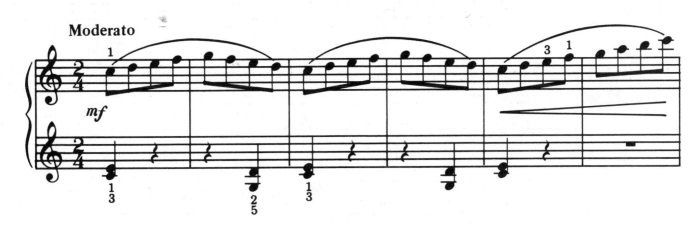

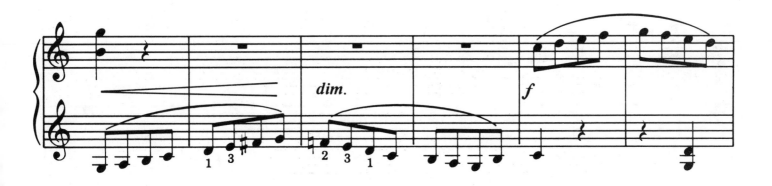

26.

10-5

Streabbog (Jean Louis Gobbearts)

Allegro moderato

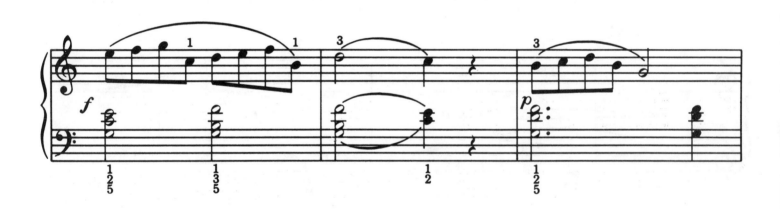

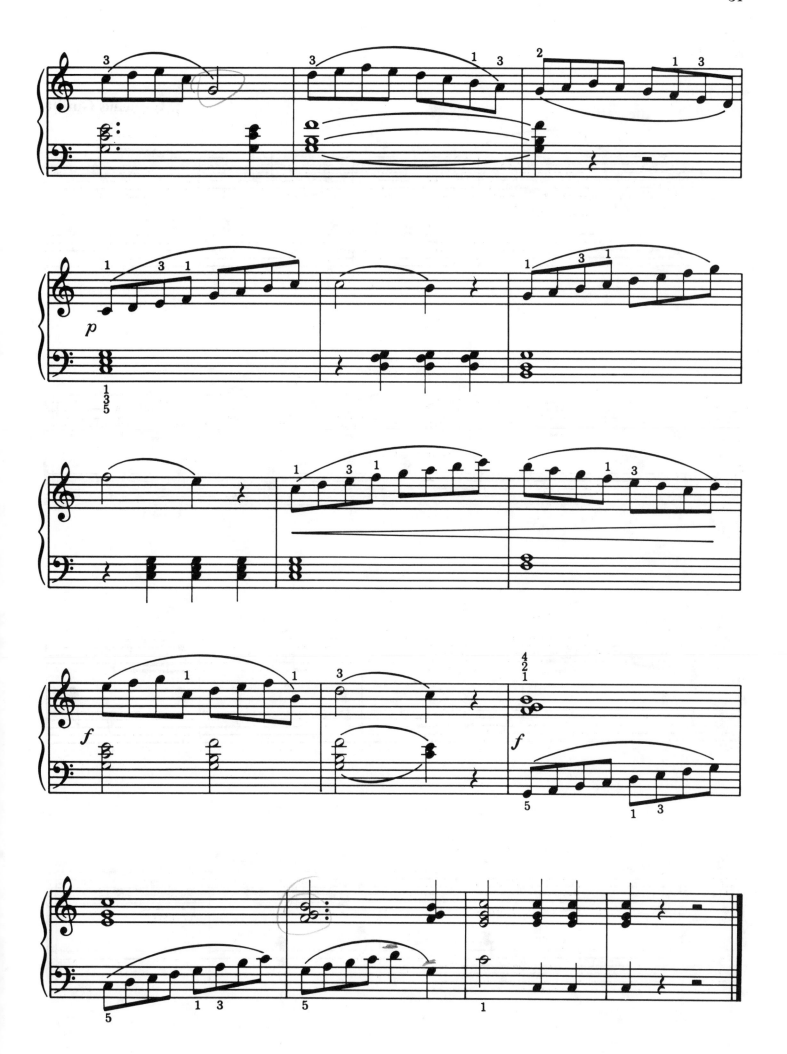

27.

Cornelius Gurlitt

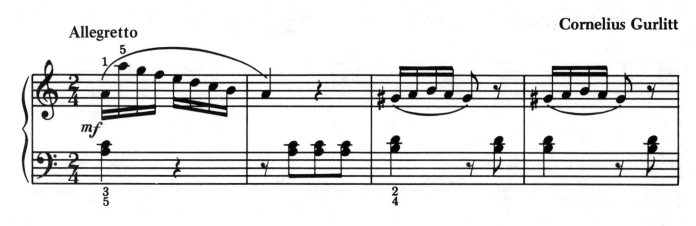

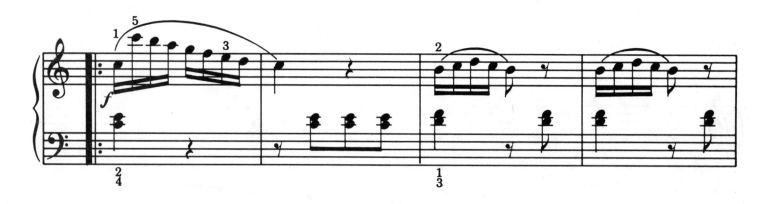
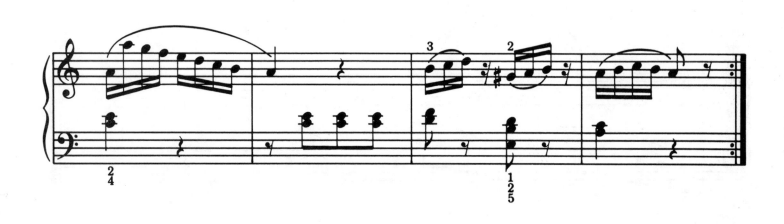